How Does My Garden Grow?

By JoAnne Nelson • Pictures by Shirley Beckes

MODERN CURRICULUM PRESS

PROJECT DIRECTOR: Judith E. Nayer
COVER DESIGN: Elaine A. Groh

Published by Modern Curriculum Press

 Modern Curriculum Press, Inc.
A division of Simon & Schuster
13900 Prospect Road, Cleveland, Ohio 44136

This edition is published simultaneously in Canada by
Globe/Modern Curriculum Press, Toronto.

ISBN 0-8136-4295-7 (STY PK)   ISBN 0-8136-4291-4 (BK)

10 9 8 7 6 5 4 3 2 1   93 92 91 90

Claudia came to my house.
She came in through the gate.
She said she had some seeds for me.
I said I wanted eight.

She told me how to plant them,
neatly in a row.
And if I took good care of them,
they soon would start to grow.

Watermelons, watermelons, planted in a row.
How many watermelons will I grow?

I bought some little radish seeds
and planted them just so.
They looked so small and tiny.
I hoped that they would grow.

Early the next morning,
I got the garden hose.
I sprinkled every small brown seed
and watered all my toes.

Radishes, radishes, planted in a row.
How many radishes will I grow?

I went out to my garden
with my little garden cart.
I planted peas and beans and onions
in rows, two feet apart.

I planted other little seeds,
each in a separate row.
There were cucumbers and pumpkins.
I hoped they all would grow.

Vegetables, vegetables, planted in a row.
How many vegetables will I grow?

Cucumbers

Plant 6-8 seeds ½-1 inch deep, in hills 4 feet apart.

Sprouting time: 6-10 days

Pumpkins

Plant 5-8 seeds 1 inch deep, in hills 6 feet apart.

Sprouting time: 7-14 days

The sun shone on my garden.
It warmed the little seeds.
I watched to see if they would sprout,
then I began to read.

I read about the way seeds grow,
how long it takes each one.
About the things that all plants need—
WATER, SOIL, and SUN.

Vegetables, vegetables, planted in a row.
How many vegetables will I grow?

I wondered when my plants would sprout,
as I fell asleep that night.
I dreamed about my garden.
It was really quite a sight.

Then Claudia came over,
and we had another look.
"See these little sprouts," she said.
"They're like the pictures in your book!"

Vegetables, vegetables, planted in a row.
How many vegetables will I grow?

Soon spring turned into summer
as I watched my garden grow.
With water, sun, and loving care,
it still seemed very slow.

Many days and weeks passed by,
as I waited patiently.
Then Claudia came back again
to see what she could see.

Vegetables, vegetables, planted in a row.
How many vegetables did I grow?

15

All the vegetables have ripened,
and now it's harvest time.
We picked a great big basket full.

MY GARDEN TURNED OUT FINE!